The Terrible Tiger

Story by Joy Cowley

"We're going to hunt
the terrible tiger.
We're not scared
of the terrible tiger.
We're not scared
of anything."

Creep, creep over the hill.

"Hello, monkey.
We're going to hunt
the terrible tiger.
We're not scared
of the terrible tiger.
We're not scared of anything."

4

Creep, creep under the log.

"Hello, bird.
We're going to hunt
the terrible tiger.
We're not scared
of the terrible tiger.
We're not scared of anything."

Creep, creep through the forest.

"Hello, snake.
We're going to hunt
the terrible tiger.
We're not scared
of the terrible tiger.
We're not scared of anything."

"That's not a snake.
That's my tail,
and I'm the terrible tiger!"

Scamper, scamper
through the forest.

Scamper, scamper
under the log.

Scamper, scamper
over the hill.

14

Scamper, scamper
back home.

"We're not scared
of the terrible tiger.
We're not scared of anything!"